D1133073

Wagner's "Ring of the Nibelung"

II

Fricka

Wotan

Sieglinde

Hunding

Brünnhilde

Siegmund

Wagner's "Ring of the Nibelung"

II

The Valkyrie
Die Walküre

adapted by
Robert Lawrence
and
illustrated by Alexandre Serebriakoff

GROSSET & DUNLAP

Publishers   NEW YORK

Copyright, 1939, by The Metropolitan Opera Guild, Inc.

Foreword

THE METROPOLITAN OPERA GUILD, Inc. is the title under which a group of several thousand people who love opera have gathered to learn more about it, and to work on its behalf. The Guild believes that some of the greatest music dramas, such as Wagner's "Ring of the Nibelung," do not unfold their beauties completely to an audience which is not prepared for them. Once the intricate story of a work like "Die Walküre" has been made clear, and the musical themes have become familiar, new curtains seem to open on the glory of the composer.

The Guild presents this book to you in the hope that from the story of Siegmund and Sieglinde and the brave Brünnhilde, and from the musical background which Wagner made for them out of the flashing sword and the leaping flames, your joy in opera may become a living thing.

Printed in the United States of America
By the Western Printing & Lithographing Company

INTRODUCTION

THE Valkyries were warrior maidens, daughters of Wotan and Erda. They numbered nine in their brave and fearless band. It was their duty to stir up strife on earth—to ride forth to battle—and to bear the slain heroes to Valhalla. Once in the home of the gods, these heroes would enter upon a new life and defend Wotan against his enemies.

Day and night, surrounded by his champions, Wotan brooded over the ring of the Nibelung. He had given it to the giant Fafner in payment for Valhalla. Bound by laws of compact, he could not take it back. And yet— if the ring should ever fall into the hands of Alberich—a terrible revenge would strike the gods!

But Wotan was cunning. If *he* could not gain the prize, neither must Alberich. And so, the god roamed the world disguised as a mortal named Wälse. He wanted to create a race of men brave enough to win the ring for themselves.

During his time on earth, the wandering Wälse became father of two mortal children—a boy and a girl. They were called the Wälsungs. Early in life, these unfortunate twins were separated from each other; their mother perished and their father disappeared. Wotan had purposely brought these hardships upon the Wälsungs to make them strong and defiant, so that they might gain the Nibelung's treasure.

In vain did the god plot and scheme. Attempting to keep the ring from Alberich, Wotan lost everything: children, honor, love. *Die Walküre* is the tragic story of his failure.

PRONOUNCING GUIDE

Die Walküre: *Dee Vahl' keera*

Siegmund: *Zeeg' moond*   Wotan: *Vo' tahn*

Sieglinde: *Zeeg' linda*   Fricka: *Frick' ah*

Hunding: *Hoon' ding*   Waltraute: *Vahl' trouta*

Wälse: *Vell' seh*   Wälsung: *Vell' soong*

Brünnhilde: *Brinn' hilda*

The Battle Cry: *Ho' yo-to-ho'*

the story of "Walküre"

THE PRELUDE

Darkness comes over the opera house. In the 'cellos, we hear a persistent rhythm, like the steady downpour of rain in a vast forest,

that becomes more threatening with every bar of music. The entire prelude keeps growing in excitement until it suggests a raging tempest. A loud report of thunder—howling of wind—and the curtain rises.

ACT ONE

Deep in the rain-swept forest, there stands a dwelling grim and warlike. Only a flickering fire on the hearth lights the gloomy chamber. And, in the very center of the room, a large ash-tree spreads its way through the roof.

As the storm rages outside, the house door is flung open and a wounded man appears on the threshold. For a moment, he glances doubtfully at the empty room. Then, he staggers forward and sinks beside the hearth.

"No matter who lives here," he gasps, "I must find rest!"

Another door, leading to an inner room, opens very softly and a young woman emerges from the shadows. It is Sieglinde, wife of the warrior, Hunding. Hearing footsteps, she thinks that her husband has come home.

"A stranger!" she exclaims in surprise. "I must question him!"

The man on the hearth looks up and calls pitifully, "I thirst!" At once, Sieglinde brings him cooling water. He drinks eagerly; then gazing at her, he asks, "Who are you, kindly woman?"

"I must find rest!"

SIEGLINDE'S PITY

In a sad, listless voice, Sieglinde answers, "This house and I belong to Hunding. You may wait till he returns."

"He will not welcome me," protests the stranger. "I am wounded and have lost my weapons."

"Wounded? Then let me help you!" Sieglinde urges.

The wayfarer declines—he is not badly hurt—but he accepts a drink of honeyed mead, which Sieglinde first touches to her lips.

THE MOTIVE OF LOVE

The stranger looks long and earnestly at Sieglinde. Rising from his place at the hearth, he declares sorrowfully, "You have aided me; for that I give you thanks. Now I must be gone."

The draught

"Why do you flee?" cries Sieglinde. "Who is pursuing you?"

"Ill fate pursues me!" he answers bitterly. "May it never cross your path!"

Hastily, the stranger goes to the door and raises the latch. Sieglinde, stirred by a force she does not understand, calls despairingly, "Stay here! Ill fate already dwells in this house!"

As the pair face each other with deep emotion, we hear in the orchestra the motive of the Wälsung race:

Hunding has returned!

The mournful quiet of the dwelling is soon shattered. Outside, a horse stamps its hoofs—stable doors are closing. Hunding has returned! Sieglinde, who dreads her savage husband, stands mute with terror. Then, mastering her fear, she strides to the door and opens it.

Hunding, armed with spear and shield, stands forbiddingly on the threshold. There is a tense silence . . . The warrior looks sternly about him. He scowls when he sees the uninvited guest.

HUNDING MOTIVE

"I will shelter you for the night," he warns the stranger, "but beware the honor of my house!"

As Sieglinde sets the evening meal, Hunding watches her closely. In astonishment, he notes how she resembles the wayfarer. "What is your name, O guest?" he demands. "Who are your family?"

"I am called Woeful," the stranger replies. "No family is left to greet me. My mother was burned to death by an enemy tribe; my twin sister disappeared. For years, my father and I roamed the woods homeless and alone."

"And where is your father now?"

"All trace of him has vanished!"

Sieglinde glances with pity at the unfortunate man. "You have come here unarmed," she says. "How did you lose your weapons?"

In answer, the stranger tells a fearful tale: how a young bride, forced to wed against her will, appealed to him for help; how he slew her cruel brothers. Vengeful kinsmen surrounded him, smashed his weapons and killed the bride. Fleeing through the forest, amid rain and thunder, he chanced upon Hunding's house.

"What is your name, O guest?"

As the stranger ends his story, he gazes in sadness at Sieglinde. His voice has become choked with grief.

"And now you know," he explains, "why I am called Woeful!"

The orchestra plays a new, sorrowful motive—the Heroism of the Wälsungs:

"You must fight me with a sturdy weapon!"

Wrathfully, Hunding rises from his meal. "You have shed the blood of my tribe!" he shouts. "In the morning you must fight me with a sturdy weapon!"

Sieglinde steps between the two men, but Hunding thrusts her away. "Prepare my draught," he commands, "and go to your room." The young wife has no choice—she must obey. Hunding follows her, and bolts the door from within.

Roused by Sieglinde's grief, the wayfarer wants to protect her . . . love has awakened within him. In deep anxiety, he sinks on a bench by the fire. "My father once promised me a sword," he broods, "that would serve in my hour of need. Here I am, weaponless, a prisoner

15

of my foe. And the woman I love is in his power." Fury seizes the stranger. "Wälse!" he calls. "Wälse! Where is your sword? Where is the weapon that you promised?"

Suddenly, the fire gleams on the hearth—it reveals a shining spot in the tree trunk. How the lonely stranger rejoices! The brilliant glow gladdens his heart. But soon the flame dies down; the room is left in darkness.

Just then, the inner door opens and Sieglinde steals from her chamber. "Quickly!" she whispers. "I have drugged my husband. While he sleeps, you must escape!"

MOTIVE OF THE SWORD

Pointing to the tree, she exclaims, "First, let me show you a weapon. Make it your own, and you will be the bravest of heroes!"

"You are the spring!"

"At my wedding to Hunding," she continues, "a mysterious wander-
er plunged a sword into the tree. When none of the guests could draw
it forth, I knew that it was meant for my deliverer. Oh, if you were
the chosen one—if you would end my sorrow!"

"I will free you!" vows the stranger.

With a roar, the huge doors of the house swing open. The storm
has passed; moonlight floods the forest. Holding Sieglinde in his
arms, the stranger gladly hails the coming of spring:

17

Allegretto

p Win- ter storms give way to the moon of love,— the spring has cast its ra-di-ant light;— it floats a-long— on gen-tle breez- es, weav-ing won-ders in the world.

"*You* are the spring!" declares Sieglinde. "In your path has come happiness. And yet, must I call you Woeful?"

"Not if you love me," he replies. "I am a Wälsung!"

"A Wälsung?" cries the woman, in highest excitement. "Then you are Siegmund! The sword is yours!"

Standing beneath the mighty branches, Siegmund grasps the gleaming hilt. "This weapon comes in my hour of need," he proclaims, "and I name it Needful!" With supreme strength, he tears the sword from the tree.

"You shall be my bride!" shouts the hero, embracing Sieglinde.

Bearing the sword before them, the Wälsungs flee from the house of Hunding into the moonlit night.

ACT TWO

THE PRELUDE

Triumphantly, the orchestra blazes forth the motive of the sword. This is followed by music describing the flight of Siegmund and Sieglinde. The prelude reaches a stirring climax as a new theme appears—the motive of the Valkyries—and the curtain rises:

On a wild, mountainous height stands Wotan, ruler of the gods. Brünnhilde, his favorite daughter, hails him from a distant cliff. She is the bravest and best of the Valkyries.

"Now bridle your horse," Wotan calls to her, "and protect Siegmund in his battle with Hunding. The Wälsung must conquer!"

In answer, Brünnhilde joyously waves her spear and shouts a piercing battle cry:

Ho-jo-to-ho!___ ho-jo-to-ho!___ hei a-ha!___ hei a-ha!___

Looking down into the valley, she spies the goddess Fricka. "Beware, father!" she warns. "Your wife is coming. How angry she looks!" Taking leave of Wotan, the Valkyrie again shouts her "Hojotoho!" and vanishes.

Fricka, goddess of marriage, now appears before Wotan in outraged dignity. "Siegmund must be punished," she declares. "He has stolen Hunding's bride!"

"He loves her," replies Wotan, "and I will not interfere."

Fricka glances furiously at her husband. "Then would you have Siegmund defy us and break our laws?" she cries.

"That is my plan," Wotan retorts. "Have you forgotten that only a brave hero—free of the gods' control—can win the ring?"

"But he is not free!" Fricka insists. "*You* promised him a weapon. *You* plunged the sword into the tree. Siegmund is only your slave!"

"Hojotohol"

Under the conquering force of Fricka's argument, Wotan becomes subdued and gloomy. "What is your demand?" he asks.

"Give up the Wälsung!" shouts the goddess.

MOTIVE OF WOTAN'S DESPAIR

With heavy heart, Wotan yields his consent. "Look me in the eye!" Fricka exclaims. "Brünnhilde, too, must turn against him—for I know that she carries out your secret wishes."

Wotan is crushed by sorrow. "How can I abandon Siegmund? He found my sword!"

"Destroy the sword!" answers Fricka. "Shatter it!"

From afar floats the sound of Brünnhilde's joyous "Hojotoho!" Nearer and nearer comes the cry until the Valkyrie stands again on the towering cliff. Fricka turns solemnly to Wotan. "Siegmund must die for my honor!" she proclaims. "Do you give me your oath?"

"I give my oath!" he mutters.

The goddess strides away, victorious. Her husband sinks on a rocky seat, overcome with grief.

"What is wrong, father?" calls Brünnhilde, rushing to Wotan's side. "Never have I seen you so troubled!"

Bitterly, Wotan tells her the whole story of his greed; the theft of the ring from Alberich—the dwarf's curse. "My work is done," he declares. "Only one thing awaits me now—my downfall!"

"But the Wälsung?" cries Brünnhilde anxiously. "Surely you will not desert him?"

"Siegmund is to perish," the god replies. "And you, O maid, shall bring victory to Hunding. Do not disobey me!" Storming up the

mountain side, Wotan raises his spear in final warning.

Brünnhilde sadly departs. "Alas, my Wälsung!" she sighs. "Must I, too, forsake you in your greatest need?"

The landscape is silent and deserted. Evening shadows are descending upon the mountain side. Suddenly, Sieglinde appears, rushing wildly along a stony path. She seems dazed with fear; her eyes are filled with terror.

"Stay!" shouts Siegmund, who is following close behind her. But the woman pays no heed. "Don't you hear the call?" she screams. "Hunding has awakened! He is sending his hounds after us!" Tottering madly, she falls in Siegmund's arms.

Night has covered the hills. While Siegmund rests upon a boulder, with Sieglinde's prostrate form at his feet, the moon rises. Its sharp, clear rays reveal Brünnhilde in full armor. *As she slowly advances, the orchestra plays two tragic motives: Fate and Death.*

FATE

DEATH

"Siegmund!" calls the Valkyrie. "You are about to die. I have come to lead you to Valhalla."

The hero looks intently at the armed maiden. "And what of Sieglinde?" he asks. "Will she go with me?"

"No," Brünnhilde replies. "She must linger here on earth."

"Then I will not follow you!" vows Siegmund.

"Hear me, O Wälsung!" proclaims the warrior maiden. "He who sent you the sword now sends you death! There is no escape!"

Bending over his sleeping bride, Siegmund bursts into heart-rending laments. He swears that he will kill Sieglinde and himself, rather than enter Valhalla. As the desperate Wälsung raises his sword, Brünnhilde's godlike poise is swept aside by pity. "Stop!" she cries. "I will help both of you to live! Farewell, brave hero. We meet again on the battlefield!"

Sultry clouds hide the moon as Brünnhilde rushes off. Siegmund looks gratefully after her. Suddenly, the harsh tones of Hunding's horn are heard in the distance. Eager to fight, the Wälsung climbs the mountain side in search of his foe.

And now Sieglinde begins to move restlessly in her sleep. Roused by violent thunder, she springs up in fear. "Siegmund!" she calls. "Where are you?"

25

The combat on the height

A dazzling ray of lightning cuts through the thick darkness. Hunding and Siegmund are seen in a death struggle atop the rocky crag. The crash of weapons fills the air.

But the men do not hear her—they are intent on destroying each other. At the height of the battle, Brünnhilde appears.

"Strike him, Siegmund!" she calls.

Hunding's death

The Valkyrie, in reckless disobedience of her father's command, is protecting the hero with her shield. Just as Siegmund aims a deadly blow at Hunding, a glowing light breaks through the clouds. It is Wotan! Raising his spear, he shatters Siegmund's sword, and Hunding stabs the defenseless hero.

Hastily, Brünnhilde gathers the pieces of the sword and helps Sieglinde to escape. Wotan kills Hunding with a scornful wave of the hand. Then all of the god's rage and sorrow rises to the surface. "Woe to Brünnhilde!" he shouts. "Her fate will be hard if I overtake her!" Amid thunder and lightning, Wotan rides in pursuit of his rebellious daughter.

Flight

ACT THREE

The prelude to this act has often been called "The Ride of the Valkyries." Based upon the Valkyrie motive, it describes the warrior maidens as they ride through the air on their way from battle. They are returning to Valhalla, and every maiden carries a dead hero on her saddle. While the music grows ever bolder and fiercer, the curtain rises.

"Hojotoho!" shout the Valkyries, assembling upon a rock that juts far into the heavens. Wild, scudding clouds course through the sky. Strange flashes of light gleam in the threatening darkness. With savage laughter, the maidens dismount from their horses and surge across a lonely wood to the summit of the rock.

Only Brünnhilde has not arrived. Her sisters are awaiting her before starting back to Valhalla. Suddenly, one of the maidens spies the missing Valkyrie speeding through the air. "How fast Brünnhilde is riding!" she cries. "Behold—she brings a live woman on her saddle! And the steed sinks to earth!"

The Valkyries rush into the wood. Immediately, they return with Brünnhilde, who is still sheltering Siegmund's bride. "Help me, sisters!" she cries. "Wotan is pursuing me!"

Terrified, the maidens draw back from her. "Are you mad?" they

The gathering of the Valkyries

"Help me, sisters!"

exclaim. "What has happened? You must tell us!"

Brünnhilde quickly explains her plight. "Hurry!" she pleads. "Look to the north and see if Father is coming!"

Waltraute, one of the bravest Valkyries, climbs swiftly to the highest point on the rock. "Storm clouds are rolling from the north," she calls. "Wotan is approaching!"

"Alas!" exclaims Brünnhilde. "If he finds Sieglinde here, he will destroy her! On whose steed can we escape?"

None of the maidens will aid Brünnhilde, for fear of risking Wotan's wrath. Even Sieglinde shrinks gloomily from the noble Valkyrie. "Why didn't you leave me to die with Siegmund?" she mutters. "There is only one way you can help me now—thrust your sword into my heart!"

"You must live," Brünnhilde cries, "for the sake of Siegmund's love! You are bearing his child!"

Instantly, Sieglinde's outlook changes from despair to radiant hope. "Save me, O maiden!" she begs.

"The storm is coming nearer," calls Waltraute from her post on the summit.

"Sieglinde must flee!" shout the other Valkyries.

At this supreme moment, Brünnhilde decides to sacrifice herself for the unfortunate bride. "You must escape!" she declares. "I will stay here and face Wotan's anger."

"But where shall I go?" cries Sieglinde.

With fearful words, the warrior maidens speak of a vast forest to the east that Wotan always avoids. There lurks the giant Fafner, guarding the ring of the Nibelung. Through the Tarnhelm's magic, he has become a ferocious dragon, filling the land with terror. No mortal ventures near the place. And yet—in this very forest, Sieglinde might be safe from Wotan.

"Then flee to the east!" Brünnhilde proclaims. "Be proud, defiant! Endure every hardship—laugh amid your sorrows! Your son will

"Be proud, defiant!"

"Where is Brünnhilde?"

be the world's most glorious hero." Holding forth the pieces of the sword, the Valkyrie intrusts them to Sieglinde. "Keep these for him," she advises. "Some day he will forge them anew. And let me name this dauntless hero . . . Siegfried!"

Sieglinde, trembling with gratitude, takes the shattered steel. Black clouds surround the height as she makes her escape. Terrified, the Valkyrie listens to the voice of Wotan, thundering above the storm. "Stay, Brünnhilde!" the god roars.

"He is here!" scream the warrior maidens. "Brünnhilde, let us hide you!" They conceal their sister and look anxiously toward the wood, which is aglow with brilliant fire. The glare comes nearer. Wotan is at hand!

Wrathfully, the god strides toward the rock. "Where is Brünnhilde?" he shouts. "Where is the guilty one?"

"Spare her!" plead the maidens. "Restrain your fury!"

Wotan angrily ignores their prayer. "Do you hear me, Brünnhilde?" he cries. "It is no use to hide!"

Humbly, Brünnhilde comes forward and faces Wotan. "Here I am, father," she murmurs. "Pronounce my sentence."

"It is already pronounced," Wotan exclaims. "Through your own choice, you have turned against me. You are no longer a Valkyrie— henceforth, be what you wish!"

"Then you cast me off?" asks Brünnhilde, in greatest alarm.

"Our bond is broken," Wotan replies. "You must leave my sight forever!"

With a despairing cry, Brünnhilde sinks to the ground. Her frightened sisters glance at Wotan in dismay.

"Does her fate distress you?" the god shouts savagely to the maidens. "Then go from here at once, lest you share it!"

The Valkyries scatter with shrieks of woe, and ride off into the stormy night. Wotan looks gloomily after them. At length, the tempest subsides. Deep quiet descends upon the rock.

Slowly and timidly, Brünnhilde raises herself from the ground. "Was my offense so shameful," she asks Wotan softly, "that it has deserved this punishment?

"O father," she persists, "silence your wrath; only tell me how I have failed you. I am not wise—but I know that you loved Siegmund."

"You know that?" mutters Wotan. "You knew the struggle that was going on within me—and yet you disobeyed?"

Gazing tenderly at her father, Brünnhilde answers, "But if you had seen the Wälsung, as I did, when I warned him of death! . . If you had heard his grievous lament! In helping him, I was true to your inmost wishes."

"You must leave my sight forever!"

As Brünnhilde speaks, the orchestra plays a motive of serene beauty: "The Announcement of a New Life." It is the life which Brünnhilde has chosen in preference to battle and death—the life of love and pity:

"You followed the path of love," Wotan declares bitterly, "while I, in sorest anguish, had to abandon the Wälsung! You broke my command, flouted my word. But the end has come. Now you must pay the penalty."

"What penalty have you decreed?" cries Brünnhilde.

Wotan looks sternly at the maiden. "You shall slumber, helpless and unarmed, on this mountain top," he replies. "The first man who wakes you will take you for his wife. You'll sit at his hearth and spin—a target for everyone's scorn!"

Brünnhilde falls on her knees before Wotan. "This one favor I ask!" she implores. "Kill me—crush me with your spear—but do not give me to a mortal coward. Surround the rock with fire so that only the bravest hero can break through the flames and win me as bride!"

Wotan's anger has softened. There remains only the terrible knowledge that he must leave Brünnhilde—leave the daughter who is dearer to him than anyone in the world. And so, he grants her plea.

"Farewell!" cries the god. "Farewell, you glorious child! No

"This one favor I ask!"

36

more will you ride with me to battle; no longer will you serve me at the feasts of the gods. You were once the pride of my heart. Now I must leave you—never to behold you again."

The feeling of sorrow—of fatherly love—grows ever stronger in Wotan. "I will build you a blaze," he declares, "such as the world has never seen! Walls of fire shall encircle your rock. Tongues of flame shall devour any coward who tries to enter. For only one hero —the noblest of all—may wake the sleeping bride!"

He embraces Brünnhilde in grief and tenderness—his farewell kiss transforms the maid from goddess to mortal. As her eyes close in slumber, he leads her to a mound beneath a spreading fir-tree. There she lies in full armor, covered with the shield of the Valkyries.

BRÜNNHILDE'S SLUMBER

With grim determination, Wotan raises his spear and strikes the

rock. "Loge!" he cries, summoning the fire-god. "Appear! Wrap this mountain in withering flame!" Three times does he give the signal. At the third stroke, glittering sparks fill the air.

MAGIC FIRE

Wotan directs the flames with his spear, until the entire rock is a sea of fire. Mounting the burning summit, the god pronounces his final word: "He who fears my spear point, shall never pass the blaze!"

As if in prophecy, the orchestra plays the motive of Siegfried the hero. Is the child of the Wälsungs destined to break through the flames?

The fire rises steadily and Wotan turns to depart. For the last time, he gazes at the sleeping Brünnhilde. Then he leaves her . . . . . . forever.

Suggested Recordings

1. The entire opera (abridged): Victor Musical Masterpieces—Albums 26 and 27

2. Act 1, complete: Victor Musical Masterpieces—Album 298

3. Excerpts (concert version arranged by Stokowski): Victor Musical Masterpieces—Album 248

4. Siegmund's Monologue ("My father once promised me a sword"), Act I: His Master's Voice-D2022

5. Siegmund's Love Song ("Winter storms have yielded to spring"), Act I: His Master's Voice-DA 1227

6. Act II, Prelude and "Hojotoho": His Master's Voice-DB4925 or Victor 1726

7. Wotan-Fricka duet, Act II: Victor-774 2/3

8. Ride of the Valkyries*

9. Brünnhilde's plea to Wotan, Act III*

10. Wotan's Farewell and Magic Scene*

    *These are best obtained as separate records in the Victor albums listed above.